New Friends and New Places

ARTHUR I. GATES
MIRIAM BLANTON HUBER
FRANK SEELY SALISBURY

THE MACMILLAN COMPANY : NEW YORK

Illustrated by
CHARLES PAYZANT AND ASSOCIATES
HELEN HANSEN, SYLVIA HOLLAND, JANET PAGE,
BASIL DAVIDOVICH, ERNEST TERRAZAS

ACKNOWLEDGMENTS

Grateful acknowledgment is made to the following authors and publishers for permission to use copyrighted material:

Abingdon-Cokesbury Press, for "Fisherman Jim," from *Fisherman Simms*, by Hazel I. Dannecker; adapted by permission of Abingdon-Cokesbury Press, publishers.

Coward-McCann, Inc., for "Davy and the Seal," adapted by permission of Coward-McCann, Inc., from *The House on the River*, by Charlotte Baker; copyright, 1948, by Charlotte Baker Montgomery.

Dodd, Mead & Company, Inc., for "The Black Cats and the Tinker's Wife," adapted by permission of Dodd, Mead & Company, from *The Black Cats and the Tinker's Wife*, by Mary and Margaret Baker, copyright, 1923, by Dodd, Mead & Company, Inc.; for "How the Hen Got Her Speckles," adapted by permission of Dodd, Mead & Company, from *Fairy Tales from Brazil*, by Elsie Spicer Eells, copyright, 1917, by Dodd, Mead & Company, Inc.

Doubleday & Company, Inc., for "Humpy, the Baby Camel," adapted by permission of Doubleday & Company, from *Humpy, Son of the Sands* by Hamilton Williamson, copyright, 1937, by Berta and Elmer Hader; for "Polly and the Captain," adapted by permission, from *Andy and Polly*, by Rhea Wells, copyright, 1931, by Doubleday & Company, Inc.

Grosset & Dunlap, Inc., for "Good Little Train!" adapted by permission, from *The Little Train That Saved the Day*, by Charlotte Steiner; copyright, 1947.

Henry Holt and Company, Inc., for "The Pasture," by Robert Frost, reprinted by permission, from *Complete Poems of Robert Frost, 1949*, by Robert Frost; copyright, 1930, 1949, by Henry Holt and Company, Inc.

ACKNOWLEDGMENTS *(cont.)*

David McKay Company, for "The Blow-Away Hat," adapted by permission, from *The Blowaway Hat*, by Leone Adelson; copyright, 1946, by Leone Adelson.

The Macmillan Company, for "The Sun Is First to Rise," by Elizabeth Coatsworth, reprinted by permission, from *Summer Green*, by Elizabeth Coatsworth, copyright, 1948, by The Macmillan Company; for "Little Helicopter," adapted by permission, from *Little Helicopter*, by Reed Kinert, copyright, 1947, by The Macmillan Company; for "Who Has Seen the Wind?" by Christina G. Rossetti, reprinted from *Sing – Song*, by Christina G. Rossetti.

The Marcel Rodd Company, for "Little Goat," adapted by permission, from *Cancan*, by Fritz Willis; copyright, 1945.

G. P. Putnam's Sons, for "Hercules, the Fire Engine," adapted by permission, from *Hercules: The Story of an Old-Fashioned Fire Engine*, by Hardie Gramatky; copyright, 1940, by Hardie Gramatky; used by courtesy of G. P. Putnam's Sons.

Stories

Fun and Friends

The Blow-Away Hat

Mother's New Hat

Mother and Father and Bobby were ready to go out for a walk.

Mother put on her new hat. "Do you like my new hat?" she asked.

"It is very pretty," said Father.

"Oh, Mother, it is beautiful!" said Bobby. "I like the pretty flowers on it."

"I do, too," said Mother. "I think flowers on a hat are nice."

They all looked at the flowers on Mother's hat. There were red flowers, yellow flowers, and blue flowers on Mother's new hat.

8

When they went outdoors, Father said, "My, what a wind there is today! Look at the way it blows things around!"

"I like the wind," said Bobby. "I like to see it blow. Father, can the wind blow everything?"

"Oh, no!" said Father. "It can't blow everything. It can't blow its nose."

They all laughed. Bobby laughed and laughed and laughed. He liked the funny things Father said. Father always said something funny when they went out for a walk.

All at once the wind started to blow the flowers on Mother's hat. Up and down went the heads of the flowers. The wind blew again. From side to side went the flowers, faster and faster.

The wind blew and blew until it blew the hat right off Mother's head! Up, up it went.

"Oh!" said Mother. "My new hat!"

"I will get it for you, Mother," cried Bobby, and he ran and jumped as high as he could.

He thought he had it, but just then the wind blew again. Higher and higher went the hat. Bobby ran as fast as he could, but the wind was faster. On and on went the hat. It turned over and over in the wind like a balloon.

A boy came by. "I will get the hat for you," he called to Bobby.

The boy started down the street after the hat. Down the street came Bobby, running after the boy. But it did no good to run after the hat. The wind went faster and faster, and faster and faster went the hat.

Then the wind blew the hat up as high as the top of a house. The wind stopped, and down to the street came the hat.

Just as Bobby and the boy came to the hat, the wind started up again. Away went the hat.

All at once Bobby and the boy could not see the hat at all.

"I am sorry," said the boy. "We can't get the hat. It is gone."

"I must get it," said Bobby. "It is Mother's new hat. I must find it."

Bobby Did It

Bobby and the boy went on down the street, looking everywhere for the hat. They could not see it anywhere.

All at once Bobby saw an opening that went down under the street. By the opening he could read:

MEN WORKING

A policeman was near the opening. He was there to keep the cars from coming too near the opening in the street.

When the policeman had stopped all the cars, Bobby ran up to the side of the opening.

"Here, boy!" called the policeman. "Don't go too near there!"

"I just want my mother's hat," said Bobby.

The policeman laughed. "Your mother's hat is not down there. It is just Jim, working under the street."

"But my mother's hat is down there. I know it is," said Bobby.

"Oh, no!" said the policeman. "Your mother's hat is not down there. But we will ask Jim about it."

"Oh, you, Jim!" the policeman called down the opening. "Come on up here!"

"Oh, you, up there!" Jim called back. "Something came down on my head. Get back. I am coming up."

Then Bobby saw some flowers coming up out of the opening. Under the flowers he saw a man's head.

The policeman gave one look at Jim and started to laugh. He laughed and laughed. He could not stop laughing.

A man in a car saw Jim, and he started to laugh. A woman in another car saw Jim, and she started to laugh.

"Where did you get that hat?" the man called to Jim. Then he started to laugh again.

But Bobby did not laugh at Jim. He was too surprised and glad to see his mother's hat.

"Thank you, Jim," said Bobby. "Thank you for finding Mother's hat."

"I did not find it," said Jim. "It just came down on my head. But the hat is all right. Take it to your mother."

"Thank you, Mr. Policeman," said Bobby. "Thank you for helping me find Mother's hat."

"That is all right," said the policeman. "You were the one who found it."

Bobby ran to the boy. "I have Mother's hat," he said. "Thank you for helping me."

"Oh, I did not do anything," said the boy. "I just helped you run."

Bobby had the hat, but the wind started to blow it again.

"Oh, no, you don't, Wind!" Bobby said. "You will not play another trick on us. You will not get this hat. I will take it to Mother."

Bobby ran down the street as fast as he could go. On a street near by, he found his father and mother.

"Look, Mother!" he cried. "I have your hat!"

Mother was very surprised and glad to get her new hat back again. "Thank you, Bobby, thank you," she said.

Mother put the hat on her head. The wind started to blow the flowers again. But this time he could not get the hat off Mother's head.

Bobby laughed. "You can't get that hat again, Wind!" he said.

The wind did not get Mother's hat again. Mother and Father and Bobby went on and had a nice, long walk.

17

Who Has Seen the Wind?

Who has seen the wind?
　　Neither I nor you;
But when the leaves hang trembling,
　　The wind is passing through.

Who has seen the wind?
　　Neither you nor I;
But when the trees bow down their heads,
　　The wind is passing by.

Where Is Little Goat?

"Little Goat, your dinner is ready," called Mother Goat. "Come and eat your dinner right now!"

Little Goat did not come. His mother called again and again, but Little Goat did not come. He did not even call back and tell his mother where he was.

Little Goat did not even know his mother was calling him. He was away over at the other end of the farm.

Little Goat and his mother lived on a very big farm. There were many horses on the farm. There was a pony, too. The horses and the pony had to eat, so the farmer had big fields of corn. There was field after field of corn.

Little Goat did not like corn, but there were many green things on the farm he could eat. His mother saw to it that Little Goat had green things to eat. He liked them, but today he was thinking of other things.

Over at the far end of the farm was something Little Goat wanted to see. He had been there all morning.

By the side of a big field some men had
been working all morning. They had put
up a big sign.

The men had gone, but Little Goat was
there, looking at that sign. He walked
in front of the sign. He walked back of
the sign. He walked all around that sign.

There was something on the sign that
Little Goat liked to look at. He wanted
to find out all about it.

Right on that sign was another little goat.

"He looks just like me," said Little Goat. "What is he doing up there?"

Little Goat looked and looked, and then he saw what the other little goat was doing. The other little goat was eating a tin can!

EAT
Hill's Best Corn
in the Blue Cans
Even the can is good enough to eat

Little Goat could not read, but he could see the goat on the sign. He saw the goat eating the tin can.

"Oh, my!" said Little Goat. "The tin can looks good. I want a tin can to eat. That is what I want for dinner. I am going to tell my mother right now."

Away he ran.

Even the can is good e

E
Hill's
in the

The New Dinner

On his way to his mother, Little Goat saw Mr. Horse. Mr. Horse was ready to eat his dinner.

"What are you going to have for dinner, Mr. Horse?" asked Little Goat.

"Corn," said Mr. Horse, "good yellow corn."

"That is not much of a dinner," said Little Goat. "I am going to have a fine dinner. I am going to eat a tin can!"

"I don't think I would like a tin can for dinner," said Mr. Horse.

"How do you know?" asked Little Goat. "Did you ever eat a tin can?"

"No," said Mr. Horse, "and I am not going to."

"Well, I am," said Little Goat.

And away he went.

Through a big field ran Little Goat. Near the end of the field, Little Goat saw Mrs. Hen and her chickens eating their dinner.

"Well, well!" said Little Goat. "You are eating corn, too. That is not a good dinner. Do you know what I am going to have for dinner? I am going to have two tin cans, maybe three tin cans!"

Mrs. Hen did not so much as look at Little Goat. She and her chickens went on eating their dinner.

Then Little Goat saw Mrs. Cat. She was having a good time eating her dinner.

Little Goat laughed at Mrs. Cat and her dinner. "You don't know what a good dinner is," he said. "I am going home and eat four tin cans for my dinner!"

Mrs. Cat had no time for Little Goat. She went right on eating her dinner.

Little Goat was in a hurry to get back to his mother, so he did not even stop to talk to the pigs. He did not even ask them what they were having for dinner.

At last Little Goat came to his mother.

"Little Goat," she said, "did you know that I have been calling you to dinner?"

"No, Mother," said Little Goat, "but I am ready now. I want five tin cans for dinner today. Let me have one, two, three, four, five tin cans for my dinner!"

"Well, well!" said Mother Goat. "Goats don't eat tin cans. That is just talk. Come on and eat these good green things for your dinner."

"No, no, Mother!" said Little Goat. "Please, may I have just one tin can?"

"You won't like it," said Mother Goat.

"How do you know I won't like it?" asked Little Goat. "How do you know I won't like a tin can if I don't try it?"

"All right! All right!" said Mother Goat.

So Mother Goat brought Little Goat a tin can and put it down in front of him. It was a new clean tin can.

"Here you are, Little Goat," she said.

Little Goat started to eat the tin can.
He worked, and worked, and worked, at
that tin can. He tried, and tried, and
tried.

Little Goat got angry. He tried again
to eat the tin can, but he could not do it.
Then he got very angry.

All at once he ran out of the field, down
the road, and away over to the other end
of the farm.

His mother saw him go. "Well, well!"
she said. "What is he going to do now?"

Even the can is good enough to eat

EAT
Hill's Best Corn
in the Blue Cans

It was not long until Little Goat came back. He was looking very pleased.

His mother asked where he had been, and he said, "I went over to that sign I saw this morning. What I did to that sign would make you laugh! Now, please, Mother, may I have my dinner?"

Little Goat got his dinner. This time he thought a dinner of green things was the very best dinner a goat could have.

So you must not ever tell Little Goat
that goats eat tin cans. If you do, do
you know what he will do to you?

This is what he will do.

To be read to children

The Pasture

I'm going out to clean the pasture spring;
I'll only stop to rake the leaves away
(And wait to watch the water clear, I may);
I shan't be gone long. — You come too.

I'm going out to fetch the little calf
That's standing by the mother.   It's so young,
It totters when she licks it with her tongue.
I shan't be gone long. — You come too.

31

Fisherman Jim

A Good Friend

Fisherman Jim lived in a little white house. Billy and Susan lived near by.

Every day Fisherman Jim gave Billy and Susan some nice fish. They liked to eat fish.

"We are glad you are our friend, Fisherman Jim," said Billy and Susan. "You are a good friend."

Every day Fisherman Jim would go to the lake to catch fish. Every night he would bring his catch of fish to town and sell the fish to the stores. But Fisherman Jim would always keep some of the best fish for his friends.

He gave fish to Billy and Susan. He gave fish to the old woman who lived down the street. He gave fish to the little boy who had to stay in bed.

He had many friends. They all said, "Fisherman Jim is a good man. We are glad he lives here and is our friend."

Fisherman Jim's house was not far from Billy and Susan's house. But it was far from the lake where he went to catch fish. It was three miles to the lake.

Every morning Fisherman Jim took his fishing things and went to the lake. He took two baskets with him. In one hand was a big basket for the fish. In the other hand was a little basket with his dinner.

As he walked the three miles to the lake, Fisherman Jim would see many of his friends. They always called to him and said, "Catch many fish, Mr. Jim. We like your fine fish."

Fisherman Jim at Work

On his way to the lake, Fisherman Jim saw Mr. Black. Mr. Black had a store in town. Fisherman Jim sold fish to Mr. Black. Mr. Black sold the fish in his store.

"Catch many fish today, Jim," said Mr. Black. "But don't give so many of them away. I can get you money for them."

Fisherman Jim laughed and went on to the lake. He fished all morning. Then he sat down under a tree by the lake to eat his dinner.

A little puppy dog came up and asked for some of Jim's dinner. Jim put out his hand and gave the puppy something to eat.

"Bow-wow! Thank you!" said the dog.

Fisherman Jim looked up. A big yellow cat sat in the tree over his head.

"Well, yellow cat," he said, "would you like me to give you some dinner, too? I think a little fish would be nice for your dinner."

He took a little fish out of his other basket and gave it to the yellow cat. She did not tell him "Thank you," but she ate it all up.

Jim ate all of his dinner, too. Then he went back to work catching more fish. By night he had a big basket of fish. They were very good fish.

That night Jim took the basket of fish to Mr. Black's store. But he did not let Mr. Black have all the fish in the basket. "I must keep some for my friends," he said.

On the way home, he gave fish to many of his friends. At last he came to Billy and Susan's house.

Billy and Susan ran out of the door to see him. "Hello, Mr. Jim!" they cried. "Did you catch many fish today?"

"Yes, Billy and Susan, I did," said Fisherman Jim. "I caught a big basket of fish today."

He showed them the basket, but by now there were just four fish in the basket. He gave Billy and Susan two fish. He took the other two fish home for his own dinner.

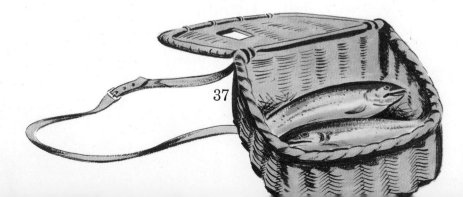

Before Fisherman Jim went to bed, he started to think.

"If I lived near the lake," he said to himself, "I would not have to walk three miles to work. I would not see so many of my friends, and I would not give away so many fish. I could sell them."

He said these things to himself again and again before he went to sleep.

Fisherman Jim's Houses

The next morning Fisherman Jim saw
a little house that was nearer the lake.
No one lived in it.

"Well, well!" said Fisherman Jim to
himself. "This house is just two miles
from the lake. I think I will take it."

So he took the house. He did not have
to walk so far to work. He did not see
so many of his old friends. He had more
fish to sell.

Before long, Fisherman Jim saw another house. It was in the forest. All around it were big trees. It was just one mile from the lake. No one lived there.

"That is a good house," said Fisherman Jim. "It is very little, but it is just one mile from where I catch fish. I think I will take the house."

So Fisherman Jim did just that.

Now he caught more fish, and he sold more fish.

It was not long until Fisherman Jim said to himself. "Why do I walk one mile to my work? Why don't I get a house right by the lake? Then I will have more time for fishing."

The next house Fisherman Jim found was right at the side of the lake. It was not a very good house, but he took it.

Now Fisherman Jim was all by himself. No one lived near him. He was too far away for any of his old friends to come to see him. All day long he fished, and he sold all the fish he caught.

Billy and Susan were sorry they could not see Fisherman Jim. They thought about him every day.

The old woman who lived down the street never ate fish now. She had no money to get fish.

The little boy who had to stay in bed asked his mother, "Why do we never see Fisherman Jim? I wish he would come to see me. I liked his fish, but I liked Fisherman Jim himself, too."

His mother could not tell him why Fisherman Jim did not come to their house. Not one of Jim's friends knew why they never saw him.

Fisherman Jim was very busy out at the lake. He caught many fish, but he was not happy.

"I am busy every day," he said, "but it is no fun to catch fish now. I have lost all my friends. It is not right to live without friends."

Fisherman Jim was very sorry for himself. Then he started to think about Billy and Susan and his other old friends. "What are they doing now?" he thought.

The next morning Fisherman Jim said, "This is no way to live. It is no fun to live without friends. I want my old friends. I know what I will do. I will go back to my little white house."

43

Fisherman Jim went back to the little white house. Every day he walked three miles to work. Every night he brought back a big basket of fish. Every night he gave some of the fish to his friends.

"Now I can help my friends," he said. "Now it is fun to work and fish."

Fisherman Jim was a happy man now. Never again did he live anywhere but in his little white house.

Engines at Work

45

Good Little Train!

The Picnic Train

All the boys and girls in Watertown were up early.

"We can't sleep any longer," they said. "Today is the day of the picnic. We want to get started early."

"We can't go until the train is ready," said the fathers and mothers. "Don't you know that this year we have a train to take us to the picnic?"

"Oh, yes!" said the boys and girls. "The picnic train! This year we have a picnic train!"

Every year in the summer the people of Watertown went on an outing. They went to a beautiful lake for a day.

This year so many people wanted to go that the fathers got a train to take them. The train was going to run just for people going to the picnic. It would take them to the lake in the morning. At night the train would come and bring them back home.

All the boys and girls thought it was fun to have a picnic train. All over Watertown, boys and girls and mothers and fathers were busy. They wanted to be ready to go to the picnic.

They would have a fine day at the lake. They would fish, and they would swim. The mothers had big picnic dinners ready.

The boys and girls thought picnic day was the best day of the year. This year it would be all the more fun because they could ride on the picnic train.

Funny Little Train

All the boys and girls liked the train ride. The picnic train was a good train with red and green places for people to sit. The boys and girls liked the picnic train because it was fast. "See our train go!" they said.

On the way to the picnic they saw another train. It was a funny train, little and black and very old. It did not go fast. It did not carry people, just things.

The little train stopped to let the picnic train go hurrying by.

"Clang, clang!" said the big train. "Get out of my way, little one! You know I always go first because I carry people. You can only carry things."

"What of it?" the little train called back. "What if I do only carry things? People want the things I carry. Go on your way, big boy! You have your work to do, and I have my work to do."

While the boys and girls were at the picnic, having fun, the smoky little train was working. It was not new. It was not fast. It did not go very far from home. But it did its work well and had many friends.

A Day's Work

Every morning early, the little train started out from the city. While people were sleeping, it started out for its day's work.

At first it had very little in its cars. The cars made a funny noise as they rode back of the engine. But that was not for long.

Out into the country went the little train. Its first stop was near some farms. The farmers were at the stop when the little train got there.

"Good morning, Mr. Trainman," said one of the farmers. "I have some corn for you to take to the city."

The farmer put the corn in one of the train's cars. "It is good corn," he said. "It will sell for good money in the city."

Next came Farmer Green. He had some pigs to send to the city. The pigs made funny noises. "Oink! Oink!" they said. They did not want to get into the car that was ready for them. But in they went.

Another farmer had hens and chickens and eggs to send to the city. He and the trainman put the eggs on the train with care. Then they put the hens and chickens on the train. The hens were angry. "Cluck! Cluck!" they said.

The little train started.

"Cluck! Cluck!" said the hens.

"Oink! Oink!" said the pigs.

"Choo-choo! Choo-choo!" said the little engine. Away went the little train.

On through the country went the little train. Farmer White was at the next stop. He had cows on his farm, so he had cans of milk to put on the train.

Farmer White and the trainman put the big cans of milk into the car just back of the engine. Splash, splash went the milk in the cans. All the while, the hens and chickens and pigs made all the noise they could.

"Cluck! Cluck!" said the hens.

"Oink! Oink!" said the pigs.

Farmer White laughed at the noise, and even the trainman had to laugh.

"We always carry things on this train that make a noise," said the trainman.

"By the way, Mr. White," said the trainman. "I brought something for you. It came from a store in the city. It has your name on the paper."

"It must be the new saddle," said Farmer White. "It is a surprise for my little boy. I had to send away for it. Thank you for bringing it today, Mr. Trainman."

"My little train and I are glad to help," said the trainman.

Farmer White went to his wagon and brought back something for the trainman.

"It is a cake," said Farmer White. "My wife made it for you."

"Thank you," said the trainman, "and thank Mrs. White. You have a fine wife. We must go now. Good-by."

Away went the little train.

The End of the Day

The little train did not stop any more. Back to the city it went. It took the milk, chickens, eggs, and pigs to the city. The people in the city could not do without these things.

Then the little train started back to Watertown. It was almost night by then.

On the way to Watertown, the little train went by the lake.

"My, my, a picnic!" said the little train to himself. "I like picnics. The people must be having fun."

But when he came nearer, the train saw that the people were not having any fun at all. They all looked very angry. The boys and girls were almost ready to cry.

"Oh, my! They are the people who were on the big train that went by me this morning," thought the little train. "Why don't they go home? Where is the picnic train?"

That is just what the boys and girls and their mothers and fathers wanted to know.

"Where, oh, where, is that picnic train?" they asked. "We are tired and want to go home. Where is that train? It should have come for us long before this. We should be at home by now."

Then the little train heard the people cry to him. "Stop, little train, please stop!" they said. So the little train stopped.

The people climbed on the little train. A man who worked for the trains had gone to the picnic. He told the trainman of the little train that it was all right. "Please take us all to Watertown," he said.

The trainman opened the cars and helped the boys and girls and their mothers and fathers get on. My, the people looked funny as they climbed on the train! They had their fishing things and their dinner baskets, but they all climbed on. They were not angry now. They were all laughing.

Some of the people got into the cars. Some got on top of the cars. Some rode on the engine.

The little train was very happy as it started to Watertown. It was not fast. It did not have pretty red and green places for the people to sit, but it could go.

On the way to Watertown, the little train and the people saw the picnic train. But it was not running. It could not go.

Right by the big picnic train went the funny little train.

As it went by, the little train called out, "Who is the best train now? I am carrying people, see? You are not even carrying things. Get out of my way! Choo-choo! I have work to do!"

All the way home, the little train said, "Choo-choo! I have work to do!"

The boys and girls on the train heard the engine talking. Then they sang with the engine.

"Choo-choo! Choo-choo! Little train has work to do!" they sang. "Funny little train! Work to do! Good little train! Work to do! Choo-choo! We like you! Good little train with work to do!"

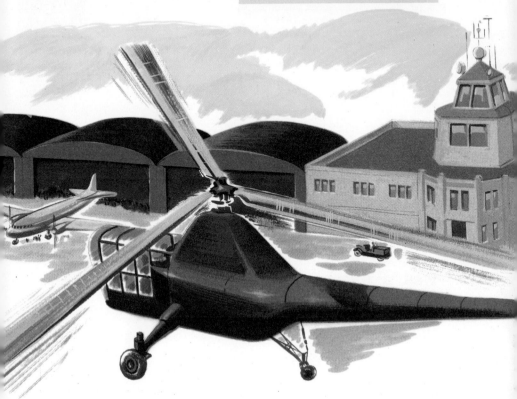

Funny Little Airplane

One day at a big field, a funny airplane came down. It was little and red, and it could fly straight up and straight down.

"What a funny airplane that is!" said all the other airplanes at the field.

One of the planes that was so surprised was a big plane that could carry many people. He was talking to a little fast plane at his side.

"I have never seen an airplane like that," said the big plane. "That little thing can go straight up in the air, and it can come down that way, too."

"Oh, no! That cannot be!" said the fast plane. "Everyone knows airplanes can't go straight up in the air. We have to run, and then climb, to get up in the air."

The big plane laughed. "Look and see," he said. "Here it comes, straight down. It is coming right at you."

"Oh, my!" the other airplane said. "I can't run away. My engine is not turning. Where is my pilot?"

"Don't be afraid," another plane called out. He was a very big plane and had four engines. He had been everywhere and knew what he was talking about.

"That little red thing up there does not have to have much room," he said. "It comes straight down and stops. It is a helicopter."

Most of the planes on the airfield had never heard of a helicopter.

"Helicopter!" they said. "What a funny name! But it would take a funny name for that funny thing."

No Wings

The big airship with the four engines would soon be ready to fly over water. He had gone over water before and had seen many places. He had seen many planes, too. He knew all about helicopters.

Most of the other planes had not even heard the name, and not many of them had seen a helicopter before. They did not like its looks.

"Why, it has no wings!" they said. "It has one engine, but no wings. What are the funny things on its head and at the back? They look like arms, and the arms turn around and around! We don't see how it can fly at all."

"But it does fly," said the big airship. "Look, it is coming down now."

When he got down, Little Helicopter was ready to make friends with the other planes.

"How do you do?" he said to them. The other planes would not talk to him, but he heard what they said about him. He did not like it.

"I can fly and fly well!" he cried. "Just look at me!"

Then straight up in the air he went. He flew over the airfield. Then back he flew and came straight down to the ground in front of the other planes. Even then they would not talk to him.

Little Helicopter at Work

Little Helicopter was a busy little plane. Every day he had work to do.

Some of the time, he was a postman. The big planes brought letters from far-away places to the airfield. Little Helicopter took the letters from the airfield into the city.

The big planes had to have a big airfield to come down on. The airfield was out in the country where there was room. The big planes could not go into the city.

Before Little Helicopter came, cars took the letters into the city. Now Little Helicopter took them. He could go faster than a car. He was up in the air and did not have to stop for lights on the streets.

When Little Helicopter got to the city, he flew to a big building. That was where he was to leave the letters.

He did not even have to come down to the ground to leave the letters. He stopped in the air right over the building. Then the men on the top of the building took the letters Little Helicopter had brought.

As they went back to the airfield,
Little Helicopter's pilot talked to him.

"I like you, Little Helicopter," said the
pilot. "I like the way you can stay in the
air without flying. It is not hard to leave
the letters on the big building because
you can stay in the air in one place. It
is not hard to do anything with you. I
like you more than any plane I ever flew."

Little Helicopter was very happy because
his pilot said nice things to him. Now
he did not care so much what the planes
at the airfield said.

Little Helicopter and his pilot took
letters into the city every day. They had
other work to do, too.

Some days, they helped farmers take
care of their trees. Once they helped
put out a forest fire.

The farmers liked Little Helicopter.

"You can do many hard things for us,
Little Helicopter," they said. "And you
can do them fast."

One day Little Helicopter went to a
new place. It was miles up in the
mountains.

There, on top of a high mountain, an
old man lived by himself. Snow was all
over the mountain. The old man could not
come down to get his letters and get things
to eat. He called up and asked people in
the city for help.

It was no trick at all for Little
Helicopter to fly to the top of the mountain.

In the snow in front of his house stood
the old man. He had on a big coat and
high boots. He stood in the snow and
looked at Little Helicopter. He thought
Little Helicopter was beautiful.

The pilot let down the things the old
man wanted. He had brought some books
for the old man to read, too.

On the way back to the city, Little Helicopter stopped in the air by the side of another mountain. The pilot looked out of his window to see some people on skis.

The people on skis in the snow thought it was fun to see a little red helicopter in the air right over their heads.

None of Little Helicopter's work was hard for him. He had a good time doing it, and so did the pilot.

"None of the pilots has a better plane than I have," said Little Helicopter's pilot.

A Call for Help

At the airfield Little Helicopter looked at the big planes that came in. He saw their beautiful big wings and heard the buzz of their many engines.

As the planes came down, they were put at one side of the field. Little Helicopter heard them talking while men got them ready for the next take-off.

The planes talked about the far-away places they had been and the many things they had seen.

"My, if I could only do things like that!" said Little Helicopter. But none of the big planes would talk to him.

One day Little Helicopter's pilot came running to him.

"Hurry, Little Helicopter!" said the pilot, as he put gas into the plane. "I have just heard that a big ship is going down out on the ocean. They are asking for help. We must save them. This is work for a helicopter. A big plane could do no good."

Other men came running. They put things to eat in the little helicopter. They put in many things that would help to save men on a ship on the ocean.

Little Helicopter took off in a hurry. He went straight up in the air. The wind was blowing, but he went right on. Up, up he went. Then he flew out over the ocean.

As soon as Little Helicopter got out over the ocean, he found he was going to meet a storm. It was this storm that was sending the ship down.

What a storm it was! Little Helicopter could not fly under it or over it. He could not fly around it. So the little plane flew straight into the storm.

The wind blew so hard that it blew Little Helicopter up and down. But on he went.

He was afraid, but he went on flying. He would not let the storm keep him from the work he had to do.

Little Helicopter and the pilot could
not see the ship. But they knew they
would come to it soon. The pilot was
talking to the men on the ship.

"We cannot last much longer in this
storm," said the men on the ship. "We
must leave the ship. It is going down.
The men are climbing into the little
boats now. One man is hurt. Come and
help us! Save us!"

"We are coming," said the pilot.

In a very little while, the pilot looked down and saw that they were right over the ship. The wind blew the ship from side to side. The wind blew so hard that a big wall of water came over the ship.

Little Helicopter saw the ship go down, down. The water came over it. Then there was no ship to be seen.

Little Helicopter saw the men who had been on the ship. Some, who could swim, were in the water. Others were in little boats. The storm had stopped now, but the water was very cold.

The pilot was busy calling other ships. Some were not far away and were coming to help. Other planes heard the pilot, too.

"A ship has gone down," he said. "We have found all the men. It is very cold. Send help fast!" He told them where to look for the men and the boats.

Ships and planes were coming, but Little Helicopter got there first. He came down and stayed in the air right over the boats.

The pilot gave things to eat to the men in the boats. He gave them coats.

Some of the men were in the cold water, trying to swim. The pilot showed them where the boats were. Soon all the men were in the boats.

"Now, I am ready to take the man who is hurt," said the pilot.

Little Helicopter went down very near the boat. The pilot opened a door in the side of Little Helicopter and took the hurt man in.

The pilot told the men in the boats that help was coming. Then he and Little Helicopter started to the airfield with the man who was hurt.

Little Helicopter went straight home, for there was no time to be lost. He was afraid he would not make it. He was almost out of gas.

Little Helicopter was so glad to see the airfield again. But when he came near, he saw a very funny thing. All the other planes were in the air. They were flying out to meet Little Helicopter.

The big plane with the four engines was there. The fast little plane was there. All the planes at the field had come to meet Little Helicopter.

The planes flew around and around Little Helicopter. Over him and under him they flew. In airplane talk they said, "Good work, Little Helicopter! Good work!"

"My, they are talking to me!" said Little Helicopter. "All the big fine planes are talking to me, and I am just a little helicopter!"

He was a very happy little plane as he sat down on the big airfield.

Hercules, the Fire Engine

When Grandfather Was a Boy

Hercules was a fire engine, an old-time fire engine. When your grandfather was a boy, Hercules was new.

In his day, Hercules was the best fire engine in the city. He went to all the fires, and he put out every fire in a hurry.

When Hercules first came to the city,
all the people went downtown to see the
new engine.

"My, what a fine engine!" they said.

"What a big engine!" others said. "No
fire will last long with Hercules."

They were right, because Hercules was
a steam engine and knew just what to do
whenever there was a fire.

There were three fine horses to pull
Hercules to the fires. One horse was
white. One horse was black. One horse
was black and white. They were fire
horses, and they thought Hercules was
the best engine they had ever pulled.

When they got to a fire, Hercules
would puff steam. Then the firemen
would put water on the fire. As soon as
Hercules started puffing steam and the
firemen got the water on a fire, it was
all over.

Everyone said Hercules was the best
fire engine there ever was.

HOKY   POKY   SMOKY

Three firemen took care of Hercules. Their names were Hoky, Poky, and Smoky.

Hoky looked after the steam. He always had steam in the engine, day and night.

Poky's work was to see that water got on the fires. When they got to a fire, he had to work fast.

Smoky took care of the horses. The horses were his friends and did everything he told them to do. When they were called out to a fire, Smoky climbed up in front of the engine. "Get up!" he said to the horses. Away went the horses, pulling the big fire engine through the city streets.

Whenever the bell in the fire house
went "Clang! Clang!" the three horses
ran to Hercules.

Hoky, Poky, and Smoky came running,
too. In no time at all, they were off to
the fire.

People came out into the street to see
Hercules go by. When they could, they
went to the fire to see Hercules at work.

"What a fire engine!" people said.
"Look at the way Smoky makes the horses
run. See how Hoky keeps the steam up.
See Poky with the fire hose. He knows
right where to put the water."

"Splash! Splash!" went the water from
the hose.

"Puff! Puff!" went the steam from the
engine.

"Hercules is all right," people said. "He always puts out the fire."

This made Hercules very happy. Hoky, Poky, and Smoky were happy. The horses were all very happy, too.

All the people in the city were proud of their fire engine. Fathers and mothers were proud of him. Boys and girls were proud of him.

This went on for years. But at last the day came when people said, "We must have a new fire engine. Hercules is too old."

Then Hercules was no longer happy or proud.

Too Old

There were new men at the City Hall now. They wanted to have the best fire engine for the city that they could get.

"Hercules is too old," said the men at the City Hall. "We must get a new fire engine for the city."

"I think we should get an engine run by gas," one of the men said. "It would be better than our steam engine. Then we would not have to have horses to pull the engine. I say that we should get a gas engine."

"I say so, too," said another of the men. "Some of the people have cars run by gas. You can see them on the streets. A gas fire engine is the newest thing today. I think we should get one."

So all the men at the City Hall said they would get a gas fire engine to take the place of Hercules.

It was not long until Hoky, Poky, and
Smoky heard about the new gas fire
engine. They talked about it in the fire
house.

Hercules heard about the gas engine,
and it made him very angry. It was
almost too much for the horses. Hoky,
Poky, and Smoky were afraid.

"I don't like the looks of this," said
Hoky. "The first thing you know, all fire
engines will be run without horses.
Then they won't need Hercules, and they
won't need us."

"That will never happen," said Poky. "They will always need Hercules. There are things Hercules and the horses can do that no gas engine can do."

"You are right," said Smoky. "The horses can take Hercules places that a gas engine can't go. With the horses we can always get to the fire."

But Hoky, Poky, and Smoky overlooked one thing. The best fire engine is the engine that gets to the fire first.

Then one day something happened.

The bell in the fire house went "Clang! Clang!" The horses ran to Hercules. Hoky, Poky, and Smoky came running. They were off to the fire.

Smoky drove the horses faster than they had ever gone before. Harder and harder he drove them.

But Hercules was too late! The new gas engine got to the fire first. It put out the fire. By the time Hercules and the horses got there, the new engine was ready to go home.

There was no work for Hercules to do. Poky did not even have to pull out the big hose. They were too late. All that Hoky, Poky, Smoky, and Hercules could do was go back to the fire house.

Hercules was too old. He was not needed any more.

A Bad Time

Later that day the men at the City Hall talked it all over.

"There is just one thing to do," they said. "Sell the horses. We don't need horses to pull a fire engine now."

So they sold the horses.

That was a bad day for Hoky, Poky, and Smoky, but there was nothing they could do.

It was a bad day for the horses, too. They had to leave the fire house. They had to leave Hercules.

First to go was the black horse. He went to a park. Boys and girls rode on the back of the black horse. Men went out to the park, too, and rode the black horse.

The black and white horse was sold to a man who drove a junk wagon. All day long the big fire horse pulled the junk wagon. All over the city he went to get tin cans, papers, and other junk.

The black horse had some fun now and then in the park, but the black and white horse had a hard time pulling the junk wagon.

The white horse went to a policeman. He had a better time than the other two horses. Still it was not like being a fire horse and pulling a big fire engine.

Hercules was still in the fire house, but he had nothing to do. All day he stood there. None of the people ever saw him now. No one said, "Hercules is a fine engine."

Hoky, Poky, and Smoky still stayed in the fire house, too. They had nowhere to go and nothing to do but stay there with Hercules. They took good care of the old fire engine.

"Some day, they will want Hercules again," Smoky said. "There will be a big, big fire, and they will need him. We will be right there with Hercules when that day comes. There are things Hercules can do that gas engines can never do."

That day came sooner than Smoky thought.

Here Comes Hercules

One morning the big bell in the fire house said, "Clang! Clang! Clang! Clang! Clang!" Five times the bell said "Clang!"

"Do you hear that?" said Smoky. "That is a five-bell fire! I wish our little bells were working so we could find out where it is."

"I will run down the street, and maybe I will hear where the fire is," said Poky.

All over the city the little bells in the fire houses said "Buzz! Buzz!" The firemen ran to their engines. Every engine in the city started to the fire. Every engine but Hercules!

Poky came running back.

"The City Hall is on fire!" he cried. "It is the biggest fire this city ever had. It is the biggest blaze I ever saw."

"This is the time for Hercules," said Hoky.

"But we have no horses!" cried Poky.

"I know what to do," said Smoky. He climbed on Hercules. He pulled the big bell on the front of Hercules.

"Clang! Clang!" said the bell. It was a big clang, for Hercules had the biggest bell of any engine in the city.

Out in the park the black horse heard that bell. The black and white horse pulling the junk wagon heard it. The white horse carrying the policeman heard it.

"That is Hercules!" they thought. "We hear Hercules calling us. He wants us. We must go to the fire house right now!"

The black horse, with a man on his back, came running to the fire house.

The black and white horse came too, carrying the junk wagon with him.

The white horse brought the policeman right to the door of the fire house.

Nothing could stop them.

In no time at all, Hoky, Poky, and Smoky had the horses ready to go. The big wheels of the fire engine started to turn. My, it was good to have the big wheels turning again! Out of the fire house went Hercules. Clang! Clang!

The horses ran as they had never run before. Hercules started to puff steam. Poky had the big hose ready.

On the way they saw a fire engine. It had come to a stop. It was out of gas.

"Climb on!" cried Poky. "We need all the firemen we can get. Bring your hose."

They saw another fire engine. It was not running.

"We need your ladders!" cried Hoky. "Bring your ladders! Climb on! We are going to the fire!"

"We will get there, too!" said Smoky.

The firemen from the other engines did not say a thing, but they climbed on Hercules in a hurry.

Faster and faster ran the horses. Faster and faster went the wheels.

Before they got to the City Hall, the firemen could see the blaze. They had never seen a building burn so fast. As soon as they got there, they went to work in a hurry.

"This looks bad!" cried Smoky. "See those men up there in the windows! Bring the ladders! We must save those men!"

They put the ladders up to the windows and brought down every man.

"More steam, Hercules!" cried Hoky. Hercules puffed steam as he never had before.

Poky showed the other firemen just where to turn their hoses. Splash, splash! went the water on the burning building. The fire was so big that some of the hoses were burned through. The firemen brought other hoses and worked harder.

All the while Hercules puffed steam to make the water run faster.

Hoky, Poky, Smoky, and all the other firemen worked hard. After a while, the fire was out. They had saved the men, and they had saved the building.

Hercules, the Hero

Later the men who had been saved from the burning building came to thank the firemen.

"Thank Hercules!" said all the firemen. "Hercules did it!"

"Yes, it was Hercules," said the men. "Hercules is a hero. And we thought Hercules was too old! We are proud of Hercules, and he can work for the city always. So can Hoky, Poky, Smoky, and the fine horses! You can all work for the city as long as you live."

"What a fire engine Hercules is!" said all the people in the city. "There will never be another engine like him!"

When the City Hall was cleaned up and made new again, Hercules had a surprise.

The people said Hercules must have a home in the City Hall. So they brought him into the City Hall and put him by the front door.

He is there now. There is a sign by him that reads:

HERCULES, THE HERO

He saved many men in the big fire.

He saved our city hall.

Today fathers and mothers bring their children to see Hercules. They tell their children the story of what happened at the big fire.

The black horse, the white horse, and the black and white horse were given a good home in the country.

Hoky, Poky, and Smoky were given a good home, too. They had the thanks of all the people in the city.

"Thank Hercules!" they still say. "Hercules is the hero. Hercules did it!"

New Places

101

Davy and the Seal

The House on the River

Once there was a little boy named Davy. He lived in a house on a boat. A big river took the place of a garden in front of his house, and his house jumped up and down with the water.

Davy liked this house very much. His father called it a houseboat and liked it very much, too.

Ships going down to the ocean would pass the houseboat every day. Men rode on the ships and called to Davy as they passed.

Little boats with puffing engines went hurrying through the water, helping the big ships. They were hard-working little boats and puffed and puffed as they worked.

Sometimes men came by in row boats. They were going to fish in the river. Davy just laughed at them, because he could catch fish without having to leave home.

Davy lived on the houseboat with his father and sister. The houseboat was tied to the bank of the river. There were other houseboats near by. Mothers and fathers and their children lived on the boats. Like Davy and his father and sister, they ate and went to bed on their boats.

Behind Davy's houseboat, a row boat
was tied. Davy could row the boat. He
would take it and go to see the boys and
girls on the other houseboats.

Now, Davy's father worked nights, and
his sister worked days, so Davy knew how
to look out for himself. He could swim
and fish and row a little boat. He could
even cook, but he did not like to cook
very much.

Davy saw many funny things on the
river. He saw ducks swim by. He saw
fish in the water. One day he saw
something that was big and brown. It
could swim better than any fish, and
it jumped in and out of the water like
a puppy.

It Was a Seal

Davy first met the water animal one night when he was fishing. He heard a splash and saw something big and brown pass by him under the water. It was fishing, too.

Davy heard another splash. Then plop, the animal jumped out of the river on to the houseboat! He looked straight at Davy. But only for a very little while. Then the animal went plop, and splashed right back into the water again.

"Oh, I know what you are!" said Davy. "You are a seal, and you came up the river from the ocean to see me."

Then Davy looked around for something to give the seal to eat. "Fish is what a seal wants," he said.

Davy ran to the kitchen. Now, on a houseboat, the kitchen is very little and no one keeps fish around very long. But Davy found a can of fish in the kitchen. He opened the can.

He took the fish out for his friend, the seal. But the seal stayed in the water and looked at Davy and the fish. Davy put some of the fish into the water. The others he put on the boat near the water.

"Now," he said, "I will watch and see what happens."

While Davy watched, the seal came and ate the fish Davy had put in the water. But the seal would not come to the boat again.

At last, Davy went to bed. He let the fish stay where he had put it on the boat. "What will my big sister say about this?" he said to himself.

Davy's Friend

In the morning, Davy jumped out of bed. He ran out to look for the seal, but the seal was gone. The fish was gone, too — all of it. There was only a wet spot where he had put the fish, a wet spot as big as the seal.

The next night the seal came near. Again he splashed in the water around the boat. Davy opened another can and put the fish out for his friend.

Again the seal would not climb on the boat. But next morning when Davy got up, the fish was gone. There was a wet spot where the seal had stopped to eat.

Davy's big sister was looking at the wet spot, too. Then she said, "We are out of fish. That is funny, very funny. I know I had two cans, and we have not had fish for dinner. Davy, do you know what happened to our fish?"

Davy told his sister about the seal. Then he asked her to tell him all she knew about seals.

"Well, Davy," said his sister, "seals live in the ocean. Sometimes they swim up the river. They will not hurt you. Some seals are in shows. They do tricks for fish and make people laugh. I like seals, Davy, but you cannot give your seal a can of fish every night. It takes money to buy cans of fish. You know that we don't have much money to buy things, don't you, Davy?"

Davy was sorry, because he was sure that he and the seal would get to be friends if he had enough fish. So Davy thought and thought.

"I know that we don't have enough money to buy fish," said Davy. "But I know what I will do! I will catch fish from the river for my seal." So Davy, who knew just how to catch fish, caught a fish for the seal every day.

Every night the seal came, just as Davy was going to bed. Every night the seal ate the fish. Then back into the water he went with a splash.

Plop! Plop!

One day Davy had to go to the store for his sister. As he climbed to the bank, he heard something behind him. It went plop, plop, plop! It was not a boy. It was not a girl. It was not a dog. It was not a cat. Sure enough, it was his seal, and it walked behind him with its mouth open.

"I know what you want," said Davy. "You would like some fish."

He ran back to the houseboat and got a fish he had caught. Davy gave the fish to the seal and watched him eat it.

Then the seal stood up and flipped his front feet together. Davy laughed and said, "I will call you 'Flipper,' because you flipped your front feet together. We are going to be friends."

The seal looked at Davy and flipped his front feet together again.

Soon the seal and Davy were good friends. The seal ate from Davy's hand. He splashed around the houseboat, and every day Davy caught fish for him to eat.

Boys and girls from other houseboats came to see Davy and watch his seal eat. They caught fish for Flipper, too.

The Pet Show

One day Davy heard about a pet show. It was to be near by. All the boys and girls that lived on the houseboats were going. They took their pets with them. They took their dogs and their cats, their ducks and their chickens.

Davy was very sorry for himself. He did not have a pet to take to the show. But he wanted to see his friends' pets. After the other children had all gone to the show, Davy walked up the river bank without a pet.

Davy came to the show and looked around for a place to sit. All at once he heard a plop! Then plop, plop, plop!

The people laughed and looked at Davy. And what do you think they saw? Flipper, the seal, was coming behind Davy. Plop, plop, he came, right behind the boy! He was looking to see if Davy had any fish.

The people laughed. "Here is a new pet for our show!" they said.

Flipper liked the show. He flipped his flippers together and looked at all the people to see if they had any fish.

"Flipper is the best pet in the show," said all the people. "He must have the prize."

"But Flipper is not really a pet," Davy said. "He does not belong to me. I give him fish, but he belongs to himself."

Some of the boys and girls started to talk. "This is not right," cried one big girl, as angry as could be. "We brought pets to the show, pets that belong to us. That seal," she said, looking at Flipper, "has no right to be here. He does not belong to anyone. We cannot let the prize go to an animal that is not really a pet."

Flipper looked straight at the big girl. Then he flipped his flippers together very fast.

"See that!" cried the boys and girls. "Flipper must be a pet. He knows what is said about him."

The man and woman who were running the pet show laughed and laughed. "Yes," they said, "Flipper must be a pet. He has a right to the prize. What do you say, boys and girls? Do you think we should give the prize to Flipper?"

"Yes, yes! Give the prize to Flipper, the seal!" cried the boys and girls. "We want Flipper to have the prize."

"Very well," said the man and woman, "we will give the prize to Flipper."

The big girl who had been so angry said nothing more. All the other boys and girls were happy and laughed. At last, even the big girl had to laugh.

When Flipper heard them all laughing, he looked at them and flipped his flippers again.

"What would you and Flipper like for a prize, Davy?" asked the man and woman.

Davy looked at Flipper, and Flipper looked at Davy. Davy said, "Fish, lots of fish!"

So they gave Davy fish for his prize, and Flipper ate it right there on the river bank. Then Flipper flipped his flippers together. Back he went into the water with a plop and a splash.

119

From that day on, Flipper and Davy were the very best of friends. Every day Flipper came out of the water and walked behind Davy like a puppy. When Davy rowed his boat up and down the river to go to see other houseboat boys and girls, Flipper went with him, fishing and playing in the water.

Polly and the Captain

A House by the Ocean

Polly lived with an old ship's captain. They had a nice little house by the ocean. It was on a hill very near the water.

Their house was red and white like a ship. Around it was a little white fence. Polly and the Captain were very happy together in the little house by the water.

121

The Captain was old, too old to work.
But he liked to think of the days when
he had a big ship on the ocean. Polly
had been with him on that ship. He
and Polly had gone all over the world
together.

"It is a big world, Polly," the Captain
said. "But now we are both old, and it
is good to stay at home."

Both Polly and the Captain asked
nothing better than to stay always in
their little red and white house. But
the Captain did not have much money. "I
really don't know how much longer our
money will last," the Captain said to
himself.

The Captain made models of ships.
They were beautiful little models. They
looked like toy ships. The Captain tried
to sell them. He put a card in the
window that told about the ship models.
But not many people near there had any
money to buy them.

FOR SALE
SHIP
MODELS

122

The Captain tried not to think about the money he and Polly needed. Every day he took care of the little house. He kept it as bright and clean as any ship.

The Captain could cook. He would go into his bright, clean kitchen and cook lots of good things to eat. Polly liked this. Most of all she liked the fine cookies the Captain could make. "Polly wants cookies!" she said.

"I like those cookies myself," the Captain said.

He talked to Polly all the time, but he kept still about the money. "We both have to have something to eat," he thought to himself, "but there is nothing Polly can do to help about the money."

Looking for Treasure

Whenever the Captain said anything, Polly said it after him.

Every morning the Captain said, "We will go for a walk." Then Polly said, "Go for a walk." That is the way they talked together.

Down by the ocean they went for their walk. They saw many things brought in by the water. The Captain thought of the many storms he had seen.

"Big ships go down in storms," he said to himself. "Sometimes fine things are in those ships. Some day maybe the water here will bring in something fine. That would be a treasure. If I found a treasure, I would have the money Polly and I need."

So every day the Captain looked for treasure by the ocean.

124

One morning Polly and the Captain started out for their walk.

"Here, Polly," said the Captain, "jump up on my hand." Up on the Captain's hand jumped Polly. "Now, Polly, get on my arm," said the Captain. Up the Captain's arm climbed Polly.

Polly thought a ride on the Captain's arm was the nicest thing in the world.

Down by the water they went. The Captain looked hard for treasure. "I am afraid there is no treasure today," he said.

"No treasure today," said Polly.

"Well, Polly," said the Captain, "it is time to go home."

"Time to go home," said Polly. "Time to go home." Polly rode on the Captain's arm all the way home.

When they got home, the Captain went to the big box where he kept his money. Once, a long time before, the box had been full of money. Now there was no money in the box, no money at all.

The Captain went to the kitchen. Once the kitchen had been full of good things to eat. Now there was almost nothing. "What are we going to do?" the Captain said to himself.

Polly did not know what the Captain was thinking. She was as happy as ever.

The Storm

That night the wind started to blow. Down came the rain. The Captain stood at the window and watched the ocean. The water looked black and angry.

More wind! More rain! The ocean splashed over the little white fence. It splashed almost to the door of the little house.

"It is a bad storm, Polly," said the Captain. "It is a bad night for ships, a very bad night!"

"Very bad night!" said Polly.

Both Polly and the Captain had been on ships in storms. They knew how bad it could be for a ship in a storm like that.

Polly and the Captain sat at the window all night and watched the storm. The wind blew, and the rain came down. Once the Captain thought he heard a honk! honk! from some ship.

Every now and then Polly put her head up to the window. "Bad night!" she said. "Very bad night!"

By morning the storm had stopped. The sun came up, and the water was bright and shining.

The Captain and Polly went out for a walk. The sun was bright over their heads.

Down by the water were signs of the storm. The water had brought in a lot of things.

"I am sorry there was a storm," said the Captain. "But I wish the storm had brought me a treasure."

Up and down walked the Captain and Polly. They looked at the things the storm had brought in. There was nothing that would do them any good.

"Well, Polly," said the Captain, "there is no treasure for us."

Polly did not talk back to the Captain this time. All at once she jumped from the Captain's arm. She flew to the edge of the water. She saw something the Captain did not see.

"What is it, Polly?" cried the Captain. "What is it?"

At the very edge of the water, Polly
had found a little box. The Captain
hurried to see it.

The Captain took the little box in
his hand. He opened it. Inside was
something bright and shining.

"Oh, Polly!" said the Captain. "It is
a treasure!"

The Captain stood there in the sun
with the treasure in his hand.

"Treasure! Treasure!" cried Polly.

The Captain put Polly on his arm. He hurried back to the little house, carrying the treasure.

"Now, Polly," said the Captain, "I will go to town and try to sell the treasure."

"Sell the treasure! Sell the treasure!" cried Polly.

"You stay here at home until I get back, Polly," said the Captain.

Away the Captain went. He had a long walk to town, but he hurried as fast as he could.

In town, the Captain talked with the men at the City Hall. The Captain said he had found the treasure after the storm.

"It is yours. You can do what you like with it," they told the Captain.

132

The treasure Polly had found turned out to be really a treasure. The Captain sold it for a lot of money.

Now the Captain's big box is full of money again. He and Polly will have all they need as long as they live.

The Captain and Polly do not have to look for treasure now. But they do go for a walk by the ocean every morning. Polly rides on the Captain's arm and they talk together.

Humpy, the Baby Camel

Animals in the Zoo

Have you ever been to the zoo? Do you like the animals in the zoo?

Maybe when you go to the zoo, you can see a seal like the one Davy had. Sometimes seals in the zoo will do tricks for children who come to see them. They can do many funny tricks with their flippers.

Monkeys can do tricks, too. People who go to the zoo laugh and laugh at the monkeys.

Little pandas are nice animals to watch. They run and play almost like children. Their coats of red and black and yellow and brown are very pretty in the sun.

Maybe some day soon you can get on a bus or a subway train and go out to the zoo. It will be fun to see the bears and elephants. When you go, you should look at the camels, too.

The camels are very funny looking animals. In a country far away, people ride upon camels. They ride upon the camels just as we ride horses, or just as people in the mountains ride burros. They could not live without camels in that far-away country.

Would you like to read a story about a camel? He was a baby camel named Humpy. Here is the story.

Humpy and His Mother

Humpy had four funny feet and a hump on his back. Humpy did not think his feet and his hump were funny. He liked them, and his mother liked them.

"Take good care of your feet and your hump, little one," Humpy's mother told him. "Camels must have good feet and fine humps to live in the desert."

The desert was Humpy's home. You
can go miles and miles in the desert and
see nothing but sand. No trees, no grass,
only sand!

There is very little water in the desert.
Here and there are places where there
is water. At those places are trees and
green grass. Men make homes under the
trees and live there. But there are not
many green places in the desert, and it
is a long way from one green place to
another.

A little village stood in the green place that Humpy and his mother called home. There were trees and green grass in the little village. But all around the village there was nothing but sand.

Humpy's mother had work to do. Her work was to carry men and things from one village in the desert to another. Camels can do this work well because they can go for days without water to drink.

Camels do not work until they are four years old. Humpy was only two years old, so he was just a baby camel.

When Humpy's mother went miles over the desert, Humpy went by her side. Humpy could go without water to drink for a long time, too. It was fun for him to go with his mother over the desert sands.

The Fat One

Humpy and his mother belonged to a man who had many camels. He sold camels to people who had the money to buy.

One day a very fat man came to buy a camel. "This is the camel I want," he said, looking at Humpy's mother. "If I take the mother, do I get the baby, too?"

"Oh, yes!" he was told. "The baby will go with the mother."

The fat man gave a lot of money for the two camels.

"The Fat One must be a rich man," said Humpy's mother in camel talk to Humpy. "See the money he has. He must be a very rich man."

The fat man bought some things in the village. The things were put upon the back of Humpy's mother. She would carry them and the man across the desert to the village where the man lived.

Humpy's mother talked to the little camel. She told him they were going to a new home. "I think we will like it," she said. "The Fat One has bought fine things to take home. He must have a good home."

Humpy's mother knew they would be ready to go very soon. She took Humpy to the water.

"Take a big drink, Humpy," she said. "We may have a long way to go across the desert. There may not be any more water for days and days."

They started across the desert. The fat man rode upon the big camel's back, and Humpy went by his mother's side.

The fat man was a good driver of camels. Both Humpy and his mother were well pleased.

"It is fun to go across the desert," said Humpy. "I don't care if it is hot. I like the hot desert."

"Stay near me, Humpy," said his mother. Sometimes Humpy wanted to go faster, but his mother made him come back.

The Fat One was very much pleased with his big camel. "She is the best camel I ever had," he said. "And as for that baby camel, some day he will be a fine camel, too."

On they went. All three were happy that first day. They were having a good time as they went across the hot sands of the desert.

Wind and Sand

The next day a change came. The wind started to blow. The sand blew around the man and his camels.

Humpy walked as near his mother as he could get. He put his nose against her. He was afraid.

"Yes, Humpy," said his mother, "we are going to have a sand storm. It is going to be a bad one, too."

Almost at once everything was changed. They could not see the sun. The sand blew against them harder and harder.

The Fat One knew they were going to have a bad time. "We must do the best we can," he said.

Humpy's mother knew what to do. She called to Humpy. "Get down, little one, like this!" she cried.

Humpy's mother put her front feet under her and sat down in the sand. The man climbed down from her back and sat down in the sand, too. He sat as close against the big camel as he could get.

Then Humpy's mother told Humpy to sit down in the sand close in front of the man. Together, the two camels could keep most of the sand off the man.

Then Humpy and his mother put their noses down close against the sand. Harder and harder blew the sand storm.

Two days and two nights went by. The storm did not stop. Around the man and his camels the sand kept on blowing.

The man had brought with him a little water to drink, but by now it was all gone. Now, too, the man had started to get sick. The big camel saw that he was sick, and she was very sorry. "This sand storm must stop soon," she thought, "or we will all be sick."

By this time Humpy wanted water.

"Oh, Mother," he cried, "I want a drink of water!"

Humpy could not keep from crying.

All at once Humpy's mother put up her head. She called to Humpy. "The wind has changed," she said. "I smell water. We are not far from it. The storm will stop soon. Then we will get water. Don't cry, Humpy!"

Humpy put up his nose. He could smell water, too. "I must have some of that water," he cried.

Humpy jumped up and started to run across the desert.

"Stop, Humpy!" his mother called. "You are only a baby. You can't get across the desert in this sand storm. You will get lost. Come back, Humpy!"

Humpy kept right on going. But when he could no longer see his mother and the Fat One, he was afraid. The wind and sand blew hard against him. It almost blew him down, but he kept on going.

After a long time, Humpy saw some green trees. Then he saw green grass, and then water! Humpy ran to the water and took a long, long drink.

Humpy Is a Hero

The people who lived in the village ran out to see the baby camel. "How did he get across the desert in that bad sand storm?" they said.

A man went up to Humpy. "Where is your mother, little camel?" he asked. But Humpy could not tell him.

The men talked together. They knew a baby camel would never go out in the desert without his mother. They were sure that a big camel and a man must be out in that sand storm.

"They are sure to need help," the men said. "A man could not live long in that storm without water. We must go and try to find him."

The men started across the desert the way Humpy had come.

It was not long until they saw Humpy's mother. She was there in the sand, trying to keep the wind and sand off the man.

They brought the sick man to the village. He was a very sick man and could not have lived much longer without help.

That night in the village, Humpy and his mother heard the people talking.

"What a brave little camel!" they said. "He saved the Fat One. He came through the sand storm and got help. He is a very brave little camel."

"Did you hear that, Humpy?" said his mother. "They say you are a hero. Well, I am proud of you, too. I think you are a brave little camel."

Humpy's mother found out other things in the village. She found out that the fat man was one of the richest men in the desert. "He is a good man, too," the people said.

Humpy's mother was glad she and Humpy belonged to a man like that.

It was not long until the Fat One was well again. He was very proud of his two camels. "Both Humpy and his mother are very brave," he said. "I will give them a good home as long as they live."

The Fat One took Humpy and Humpy's mother to his fine home. There they stayed. Never again did they go out in a sand storm. From that time on, they were given everything a camel could want.

Once Upon a Time

149

The Letter

Once upon a time, many, many years ago, there was a little white hen. She was a busy little hen. She worked in her garden all day long. As she worked, she sang. She was a busy, happy little hen.

One day the little white hen was at work in her front garden. She sang a happy little song as she worked with her flowers.

All at once a wind blew across the garden. It blew a piece of paper over the fence. The paper came down to the ground at the feet of the little hen.

She looked at the piece of paper in surprise. "What is this that blew into my garden?" she asked.

At first the little hen was afraid to pick up the piece of paper. She walked all around it and looked at it.

At last she picked it up. "Why, I know what this is!" she said. "I am sure it is a letter. I can't read it, but it must be a letter."

The little white hen turned the piece of paper over and looked at the other side. She was surer than ever that it was a letter.

"Yes, it is a letter," she said, "and it must be a letter to the king. Last year when the king came to our village, people gave him letters. The letters told the king what the people wanted the king to do. There were many things they wanted the king to do for our country. This must be a letter to the king."

The little white hen was happy and
proud. "Now, even I, the little white
hen, have a letter," she said. "I am
going to carry my letter to the king.
I will go right to the king's palace and
give my letter to the king."

The little white hen knew that it
was a long journey to the king's palace.
She had never been very far from home,
but she was a brave little hen.

"I will make the journey," she said.
"I will go to the king's palace. I will
go in to see the king and put my letter
at his feet."

The little white hen got ready for the
long journey.

The Journey

The sun was shining the next morning when the little hen started on her journey. She had put the letter in the bottom of her little brown basket. She picked up the little brown basket and carried it with care. On her head was her pretty blue hat, and on one arm she carried the little brown basket. Down the road went the little white hen.

On the way, she sang her happy little song. She was very proud because she was going to the king's palace. She was proud that even she, the little white hen, could carry a letter to the king.

It was not long until the little hen met her friend, the fox. She ran from every fox but this one. A little while ago, she had helped the fox.

A farmer had caught the fox, but the little hen had helped the fox to get away. The fox said he would never forget her. From that time on, they were the best of friends.

So on this bright morning, the fox called to the hen. "Oh, little white hen!" he said. "Where are you going?"

"I am going to the palace," said the hen. "I am going to carry a letter to the king."

"Let me go with you," said the fox. "Let me go with you to the palace. I should like to see the king."

"Very well," said the little white hen. "You are my friend. I never forget a friend. Make yourself little and climb into my little brown basket."

Into the bottom of the little brown basket climbed the fox. Away they went, the little white hen, the fox, and the little brown basket. On the way the little white hen sang her happy little song.

It was not long until the little white hen met her friend, the river. A little while ago the little hen had been kind to the river, and they were the best of friends.

"Oh, little white hen!" called the river. "Where are you going?"

"I am going to the palace," said the hen. "I am going to carry a letter to the king."

"Let me go with you, kind little hen," said the river. "Let me go with you to the palace. I should like to see the king."

"Very well," said the little white hen. "You are my friend. I never forget a friend. Make yourself little and climb into my little brown basket."

Into the little brown basket climbed the river. Away they went, the little white hen, the fox, the river, and the little brown basket.

It was not long until the little white hen met her friend, the fire. A little while ago the little hen had helped the fire, and they were the best of friends.

"Oh, little white hen!" called the fire. "Where are you going?"

"I am going to the palace," said the hen. "I am going to carry a letter to the king."

"Let me go with you," said the fire. "Let me go with you to the palace. I should like to see the king."

"Very well," said the little white hen. "You are my friend. I never forget a friend. Make yourself little and climb into my little brown basket."

By this time the little brown basket was so full that they could not make room for the fire. They tried and tried, but there just was not enough room. At last they thought of a way. The fire changed himself into ashes. Then there was room for him in the basket.

In the Palace of the King

The little white hen and her friends journeyed on. At last they came to the king's palace.

The little hen was stopped at the great door of the palace.

"Who are you?" asked the king's doorkeeper in a great big voice. "And what are you carrying in your little brown basket?"

159

At first, the little white hen was so afraid, that she could not say a thing. Then she found her voice, but it was a very little voice.

"I am the little white hen," she said, "and I have a letter for the king in my little brown basket."

She said nothing about the fox, the river, and the fire she had in her little brown basket. It was well, too, that she did not say anything about them, as we shall see.

The great door of the palace opened.

"Come in," said the doorkeeper. "You may see the king. Shall I take you to him?"

"Oh, please do!" said the little white hen in her very little voice. "Please take me to the king."

Down a long hall went the doorkeeper and the little white hen. She carried the little brown basket on her arm.

"Can this really be happening to me?" thought the little hen. "I am in the king's palace, and I shall see the king!"

Her friends in the basket kept still and said nothing.

Another door opened wide. There in a great chair sat the king.

Up to the king in his great chair walked the little white hen.

"Who are you?" asked the king in a great big voice. "Why do you come here?"

"I am the little white hen," said the little hen in her very little voice. "I have come to bring a letter to you, my King."

The little white hen took the piece of paper from the bottom of the basket. She gave the paper to the king.

Now the paper had been a long time in the bottom of the basket. The fox's feet were not clean when he climbed into the basket. There were black spots where he had put his dirty feet on the paper.

The river was wet when he climbed into the basket. There were wet places on the paper.

When the fire changed himself into ashes, he burned little places in the paper.

The king took one look at the piece of paper.

"What in the world is this?" he cried. "This is not a letter. This is only a dirty piece of paper!"

The king was almost too angry to talk. The little white hen was too surprised to say anything.

Then the king turned to the doorkeeper.

"Take this good-for-nothing hen away!" he said. "Put her with the chickens and ducks. I shall eat her for dinner tomorrow. Away with her!"

Friends to Help

The little white hen heard the king say he would eat her tomorrow. Before she knew what was happening, she was out of the palace and in the king's chicken yard. But she still had the little brown basket.

All around her were ducks and chickens, and they were very angry.

"Quack! Quack!" said the ducks. "Who is this? We will not have her in the king's chicken yard!"

"Off with her head!" said the chickens. "Don't wait until tomorrow! Off with her head now!"

The ducks and chickens flew at her. They tried to hurt her. The chicken yard was a big, wide place, but the little hen could not get away from the angry ducks and chickens.

At last, an old duck tried to take the little brown basket away from the little white hen. At that, the fox said to himself, "I have waited long enough. Now is the time for me to come to the help of the little white hen."

Out of the basket jumped the fox. In no time at all, there was not one of the king's ducks or chickens left in the chicken yard.

What a noise the ducks and chickens made as the fox ran after them! The people in the palace heard the noise.

The cook ran out of the kitchen. The doorkeeper left the great door. Even the king jumped up from his chair. Out into the chicken yard they all came running.

"Catch that fox!" called the king.

"Catch that hen!" called the cook.

The fox jumped over the fence and was gone. The little white hen started to run. She ran as fast as she could, and she did not forget to take her little brown basket with her.

On went the little white hen. Right behind her came the king, the cook, the doorkeeper, and all the people from the palace.

They almost caught the little white hen. But just then the river jumped out of the little brown basket. He ran right in front of the king and all the people.

The river made himself big, so big that the king and the people could not get across.

"Bring out the boats!" said the king. "We must get that hen!"

Everyone on the other side of the river ran to get the boats. The little white hen took one look, and then she started to run again. She could see them coming with the first boat.

The little white hen ran and ran. She was very tired now and could not run fast, but she kept the little brown basket.

She came to the edge of a forest. She thought no one could find her in the forest.

But the cook saw her and cried out, "There she is! She is behind that tree!"

Then out of the basket jumped the fire that had changed himself into ashes. Right into the king's face flew the ashes. Ashes flew into the king's eyes. The king could not see a thing.

Ashes flew into the faces of the cook, the doorkeeper, and all of the people. Ashes flew into their eyes. None of them could see a thing.

"This is too much!" cried the king. "Let the good-for-nothing hen go. We will go back to the palace and forget all about her."

Back to the palace they went and left the little hen in the forest.

"Oh, oh, oh!" said the little hen. "My friends have saved me. There is nothing to hurt me now. I can go home."

When the little hen got home, people did not know her. She was no longer a little white hen. There were speckles all over her.

When her friend, the fire, who had changed himself into ashes, jumped out of the little brown basket, he flipped ashes all over the little white hen. Then all at once, she was a little speckled hen.

The little speckled hen was never white again. As long as she lived, she was a little speckled hen. Not only that, but in the years to come, all her children, all her children's children, and all her children's children's children were speckled, too.

I Saw a Ship

I saw a ship a-sailing,
    A-sailing on the sea;
And oh, it was all laden
    With pretty things for thee!

There were comfits in the cabin,
    And apples in the hold;
The sails were made of silk,
    And the masts were made of gold.

The four and twenty sailors,
    That stood between the decks,
Were four and twenty white mice,
    With chains about their necks.

The captain was a duck,
    With a packet on his back;
And when the ship began to move,
    The captain said, "Quack!   Quack!"

171

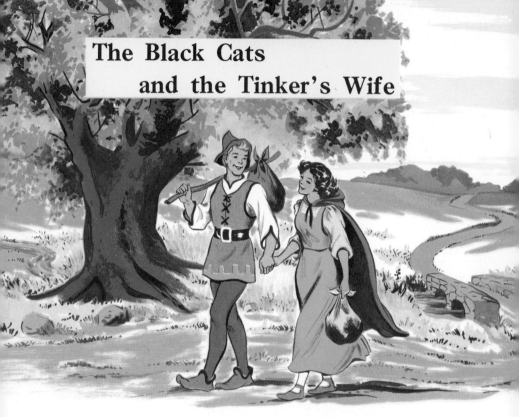

The Black Cats
and the Tinker's Wife

The Tinker and His Wife

Once upon a time, there was a tinker. He went about the country looking for things to mend. His little wife went with him.

All day they walked the country roads. At night they went to sleep under a tree or in the green grass on a hillside.

As soon as the sun was bright in the morning, the tinker and his wife would be up and on the road.

When they came near a farmhouse, the tinker called out, "Pots to mend! Have you any pots to mend? Give me your pots to mend. Pots to mend!"

The tinker was happy when a housewife came to the door and gave him a pot to mend. He mended pots well, but he could not make much money mending pots.

Everyone liked the tinker. He was a pleasant, happy man, and he sang as he worked. The people in the farmhouses were glad to see him coming down the country road.

All the boys and girls were glad to hear the tinker calling, "Pots to mend!" It was not because they had pots that needed mending, but because of the tinker's wife.

While the tinker worked, his little wife played with the children. She sang songs to them. Sometimes she would take their hands and dance with them. Around and around they danced.

The children would stop to see the tinker's wife dance. Over the green grass the tinker's wife danced like a fairy. The children thought she looked like a fairy.

The tinker's wife laughed at the thought that she was a fairy. "Oh, no!" she said. "I am not a fairy. I am just the tinker's wife. But I know a fairy story. Shall I tell you a fairy story?"

Then the children would sit down on the grass close around the tinker's wife, and she would tell them a fairy story. She knew many stories, and the children never heard enough of them.

The mothers and grandmothers would come out of the houses to hear the fairy stories, too. It was a pleasant day in any farmhouse when the tinker and his wife came.

When the tinker's work was over, he and his little wife would go away again. The children watched them as far as they could see them.

You would think the tinker and his wife could have no pleasanter way to live. But sometimes the tinker's wife was sad.

When they passed through a village, they sometimes saw an open doorway. Through the open doorway, the tinker's wife saw a pretty room. In the room a woman was busy about her work.

The tinker's wife would turn to look back at the open doorway. Then the tinker's face would grow sad. He knew what his wife was thinking.

"Will I ever make enough money to give her a home?" said the tinker to himself. He was afraid that the money he could make would never be enough to get them a home.

When the tinker's wife saw that the tinker's face was growing sad, she sang and laughed until he was happy again.

Out in the Storm

Now it happened that one day there was a great storm. The wind blew, and the rain fell.

The tinker and his wife were out in the storm. The country they were passing through had no houses. All day they walked the road in the storm. There was not a house where they could stop.

Long before night, it started to grow dark. In no time at all, it was so dark that the tinker and his wife could not see the road in front of them. The wind blew harder, and the rain fell faster.

It got very cold. But there was nothing for the tinker and his wife to do but to keep on walking in the dark.

The tinker and his wife were very
tired. He put his arm around her and
tried to help her walk in the dark.

The tinker had never wished for a home
more than he did that night. He would
have been glad to find any place to get
out of the storm.

He looked at the sides of the road.

"Maybe there is a wall somewhere,"
he said to himself. "We could get behind
that and keep off some of the cold."

But there were no walls. There was
not even a tree.

The tinker's wife was a brave woman.
She did not say a thing to the tinker
about being tired and cold and wet.
But to herself she said, "I don't think
we can go on. We will have to stop by
the side of the road. How I wish we
could find some place where we could be
out of the storm!"

That was what the tinker's wife wished
and said to herself. It was then that they
saw a light.

"Look!" cried the tinker. "There is a light on the side of the hill!"

"Some one must live there," said his wife. "We will go up the hill and knock on the door. I am sure they will let us come in out of the storm."

Up the hill they went. As they came near, they saw there was no door to knock upon. There was no house.

The light came from a wide opening in the side of the hill. They saw that it was a cave. Inside the cave they could see a fire burning.

The Black Cats

The tinker and his wife came to the cave. As they came nearer, they could see a great black pot over the fire. Near by they saw a chair.

There was nothing strange in that. But there was something more in the cave, and it was very strange. By the fire sat a great many black cats.

There were big cats, little cats, fat cats, old cats, and little kittens. All kinds of cats sat by the fire. And every cat was a black cat.

181

The tinker and his wife stopped in
surprise at the mouth of the cave. Never
had they seen so many black cats at one
time.

The cats looked up and saw the man
and woman at the mouth of the cave.
Some of them ran away to hide. Some of
them stayed, but their eyes were red and
angry in the light of the fire.

"Come and be friends," said the tinker
to the cats. But more of the cats ran
away to hide. The others still looked
angry.

The tinker and his wife went into the
cave.

"It is strange that there is no one here," said the tinker's wife. "All these cats must belong to some one."

"Well," said the tinker, "there are more cats here than I would care to live with. But the cave is warm, and we will be out of the storm."

"Oh, yes! I am so glad to get out of the cold," said the tinker's wife.

They went up to the fire. They put out their hands to the warm fire. They took off their wet coats.

The tinker's wife sat down in the chair. The tinker sat on the ground by her side.

"Oh, it is good to get out of the storm!" they said.

After a little while, one by one the cats began to come back. They sat down on the other side of the fire and looked at the tinker and his wife.

Their eyes were not so angry now.

"They will soon be friends," said the tinker's wife. "They will know we wish them only good."

First one, then another, of the cats came nearer. A little black kitten came close to the tinker's wife and jumped into her lap.

At last all the cats came back to the fire. They sat down by the tinker and his wife.

Outside the wind blew and the rain fell. But in the cave it was warm and pleasant.

The tinker and his wife sat all night by the fire. The little black kitten stayed in the lap of the tinker's wife, and the other cats sat close by.

So the tinker went down the hill to find work. He looked back and saw his wife in front of the cave. She stood there in the sun, with the kitten in her arms. All around her were the black cats.

When the tinker was gone, she began at once to clean the cave. It was not dirty, but from one end of the wide cave to the other, she cleaned. All day she worked, and she sang as she worked.

The black cats did not know what to make of this. They had never seen anything like it.

Now and then the tinker's wife would stop to say something to the cats. They listened and tried to talk to her. "Me-ow! Me-ow!" said all the cats in happy voices.

187

At the end of the day, the tinker came back to the cave. He had found work and bought good things to eat.

The tinker's wife cooked their supper in the big pot over the fire. They were happy as they ate their supper in the cave. There was enough to eat to give something to all the cats.

"Me-ow! Me-ow!" said the happy cats.

"Did anyone come to the cave today?" asked the tinker.

"No, and I am so glad they didn't," said his wife. "It is a very nice cave. I wish . . ."

Before the tinker's wife could go on, and just as she said "I wish . . . ," the ears of all the cats went up. They turned their heads to listen.

"I wish I could give you your wish," said the tinker.

"I wish," said the tinker's wife, "I wish we could live here always and that we had another chair. Then you would not need to sit on the ground."

"Well, well!" said the tinker. "That is just the wish I would wish myself."

They laughed together, and the black cats said "Me-ow! Me-ow!" in happy voices.

Strange News

After dinner the tinker and his wife sat before the fire.

The tinker's wife got out her knitting. Soon she was busy knitting blue mittens for the tinker. They both thought how pleasant it was to sit before a fire together.

"Tell me what you did today," said the tinker's wife. "Did you hear any news while you were at work?"

"Yes, I did," said the tinker. "I heard some very strange news. I passed a farm near the town. It was a good farm, but there was no one there at all. I thought it strange that a fine farm should have no one to take care of it."

"When I got to town," the tinker went on, "I asked why a good farm was without a farmer. They told me a strange story. One day a queer old woman with a very long nose came to the farmhouse and knocked on the door. Before the farmer could stop him, the farm dog came out and tried to run the queer old woman away. She got very angry and said angry things to the farmer.

"That was the last anyone saw or heard of the farmer. The people are sure that the queer old woman was a witch and carried the farmer away."

When the tinker said "witch," one of the biggest cats in the cave let out a long, angry "Me-ow!" All the other cats began to cry, too. The cave was full of one long, angry "Me-ow!" after another.

"What a sad, sad story!" said the tinker's wife.

The next day was another happy day
for the tinker's wife.

When the tinker came back that night,
the first thing he asked was, "Has anyone
come today?"

"No," said his wife, "and I am glad
they didn't. I wish . . ."

At that all the black cats put up their
ears and turned their heads to listen.

The tinker said, "I wish I could give
you your wish."

"I wish," said the tinker's wife, "I
wish that we could live here always and
that we had a little goat. The little
goat could eat the grass on the hillside
and give us milk. Then we would have
milk for the cats to drink."

"Well, well!" said the tinker. "That
is just the wish I would wish myself."

They sat by the fire after supper, and the tinker's wife was busy with her knitting. She listened to more strange news the tinker had to tell.

"In a home on the far side of the hill," said the tinker, "there is a doll that once belonged to a little girl. But there is only the doll now, with no one to play with it. The little girl made a face at the witch one day. No one has seen the little girl from that day to this."

At that, one of the little cats started a long sad "Me-ow!" All the other cats began to cry, too. "Me-ow! Me-ow!"

"What a queer, sad story!" said the tinker's wife, as she took the little cat into her arms.

That was the way it happened every day. The tinker brought back sad news that he had heard, and his wife had a wish to wish.

One day the tinker's wife wished for flowers to plant at the wide mouth of the cave. "White flowers and red flowers with their green leaves would be pretty planted here," she said.

Another time she wished for a nice bed. "But I don't really care," she said. "The cave is very, very nice as it is."

The tinker came back day after day with a sad story to tell his wife. Every day he heard of some one who had made the old witch angry and then was never seen again.

There was the farmer's wife who gave the witch a piece of cake that was burned a little. There was the little boy who called the old witch names.

As the tinker came to the end of a story, one of the black cats would cry out a long sad "Me-ow!" Then all the other cats would cry, "Me-ow! Me-ow!"

One day the tinker told of a man and woman who sat down too near the witch's cave.

"Cave!" cried the tinker's wife. "Could it have been this cave?"

The tinker did not know. None of the people could tell him where the old witch lived. Some of them thought they had seen her flying through the air at night. Where she went, they did not know.

Then It Happened

Time went on. It would have been hard to find anyone as happy as the tinker's wife. Every day she did her work in the cave. She kept it nice and clean. She sang and danced as she worked, and she was never too busy to talk to the cats and pet them.

The tinker was a happy man. Every night he found his little wife waiting for him at the mouth of the cave. He, too, found time to pet the cats.

So things went on for a long time. But the cats looked as if they were waiting for something to happen. Every time the tinker's wife said, "I wish . . . ," the ears of the cats went up and they turned their heads to listen.

The tinker's wife started to think about all the strange stories the tinker had heard. She thought, too, about all the black cats that lived with them in the cave.

One night after supper, she and the tinker sat by the fire. The little black kitten was in her lap. As she put out her hand to pet the kitten, she said to herself, "Can it be? If it should be so. . . ." Then she looked into the fire, and her eyes were sad.

At last, she said to the tinker, "What could have happened to those fathers and mothers and boys and girls that the old witch took away? And is it not more than a little strange that there are so many cats here, and all black?"

The tinker could not tell her a thing.

She looked around at the cats. Every cat was looking very hard at her.

197

All at once the tinker's wife cried out, "That is it! That is it!"

"What is it?" asked the tinker in surprise.

She did not tell him, but she said, "I have one last wish." She looked at all the black cats.

"I wish I could give you your wish," said the tinker.

"I wish . . . ," she said, "I wish all these cats were changed back into what they should be!"

And then it happened!

The black cats were changed into people. A little black cat was the little girl who made a face at the old witch. Here were the man and woman who sat down too near the witch's cave. Here was the woman who gave the witch the burned cake, and the boy who called her names. The biggest cat of all was the farmer who had the dog that ran after the witch.

They were all here, and they were people again. Oh, how happy they were! They cried and laughed because they were so happy.

They put their arms around the tinker's wife and thanked her. "You have saved us!" they said.

Then they hurried down the hill to their homes.

A Happy Home

Down the hill went all the people who had been cats. They looked back at the tinker and his wife at the mouth of the cave. "Good-by! Good-by!" they called.

Then the tinker turned to his wife. "This is the witch's cave," he said. "But what has happened to the old witch herself?"

The tinker's wife laughed. "I think I know," she said. "You know the bad storm that brought us to the cave? I think that storm must have been too much for the old witch. I think the wind caught her and blew her so high in the air that she could never come down. She won't ever come back! And the cave is ours!"

The tinker's wife was so happy that she danced over the grass. The tinker was happy and laughed to see her.

200

The tinker and his wife went back into the cave.

"I shall be sorry to have no cats," said the tinker's wife. Just then she looked down at her feet. There was the black kitten that had sat so many times on her lap.

"There is a cat that has not changed!" cried the tinker.

"I must not have wished hard enough," said the tinker's wife. She picked up the kitten. Again and again she wished that it would change into what it had been. But it did not change. It was still a cat.

At last she said, "I think you have always been a cat. I am glad. Now you can really be my cat and live with us always."

The next morning, the tinker and his wife had a great surprise. They looked out of the cave and saw many people coming up the hill.

At the head of the people was the farmer who had been a black cat. He had a little goat with him.

"We have come to thank you again," said the farmer. "But we want to do more than thank you. You wished for a little goat. Here is my best goat, and it is yours."

The tinker and his wife were almost too happy to say anything.

The man and woman who had gone too near the witch's cave brought them a fine big bed. The farmer's wife who had burned the cake brought them not only one chair, but four good chairs.

The little boy and girl who had been cats brought them beautiful flowers to plant at the mouth of the cave.

Other people in the countryside brought them fine things, too.

"I shall never wish for anything again," said the tinker's wife. "I have everything I ever wished for."

So the tinker and his wife and the black cat lived together in the cave, and they were as happy as they could be.

In the years to come, boys and girls from the farms and the town came up the hillside to see the tinker's wife. They liked to play and dance with her. They liked to listen to the stories she could tell.

Many times when the tinker came home from work, he found his wife with the children close around her. He would sit down, too, and listen to the fairy story she told.

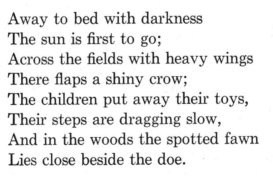

The Sun Is First to Rise

Up in the morning early,
The sun is first to rise;
The little birds begin to sing,
The farmers rub their eyes;
The rabbits hop down roads of dew,
The new-born baby cries,
And the gray kitten runs and leaps,
Chasing white butterflies.

Away to bed with darkness
The sun is first to go;
Across the fields with heavy wings
There flaps a shiny crow;
The children put away their toys,
Their steps are dragging slow,
And in the woods the spotted fawn
Lies close beside the doe.

205

Word List

The following list contains all the new words — 212 in number — that occur in *New Friends and New Places*, basal Second Reader, Book Two, of *The Macmillan Readers*. The 372 words introduced in previous basal books of the series, with the exception of sixteen proper names, are repeated, making the total vocabulary of this book 568 words. Regularly inflected variants of known words formed by adding *s, 's, ed, ing, er*, and *est*, and compounds whose parts have been previously introduced, are not counted as new words.

1.
2.
3.
4.
5.
6.
7.
8. walk
   flowers
9. wind
   can't
10. blew
    high
11. after
12. policeman
    near
13. Jim
14.
15. laugh
16.
17.
18.
19. goat
    even
20. fields
    corn
21. sign
22. tin
23.
24. well
25.
26.
27. five
    won't
28. tried
    got
29.
30.
31.
32. fisherman
    fish
33. lake
    catch
34. miles
    hand
35. sold
    give
36. ate
37. caught
38. himself
39. next
40.
41. why
42.
43. busy
    without
44.
45.
46. early
    year
47. people
    because
48. carry
49. only
    while
50. made
    country
51. oink
52. milk
53. wife
54. almost
    cry
55. should
56.
57.
58. sang
59. helicopter
    straight
60. planes
    air
61. does
62. wings
    arms
63. flew
    ground
64. than

206

65. building
leave
66. hard
67.
68. stood
69. none
better
70.
71. ocean
save
72. storm
or
73. hurt
74.
75. cold
76.
77.
78.
79. Hercules
80. steam
81. pull
puff
82. Hoky
Poky
83. hose
84. proud
85. hall
say
86. need
87. happen
88. drove
late
89. bad
nothing
90. park
junk
91. still
92. hear
biggest
93.

94. wheels
95. ladders
96. those
97.
98. hero
99. children
100. given
101.
102. Davy
seal
103. pass
row
104. sister
bank
105. behind
cook
106. met
plop
107. kitchen
watch
108. wet
spot
109. buy
110. sure
111. mouth
112. flipper
flipped
113.
114.
115.
116. really
belong
117.
118.
119. lots
120.
121. Polly
captain
122. world
both

123. kept
bright
124. treasure
125.
126. box
full
127. rain
128.
129. sun
shining
130. edge
131. hurried
132.
133.
134. Humpy
camel
135.
136. hump
desert
137. sand
grass
138. village
drink
139. fat
rich
140. bought
across
141. hot
142. change
against
143. close
144. sick
smell
145.
146.
147. brave
148.
149.
150. speckles
ago

151. song
piece
152. pick
king
153. palace
journey
154. bottom
carried
155. fox
forget
156. yourself
157. kind
158. ashes
159. great
voice
160. shall
161. wide
chair
162. dirty
163. tomorrow
164. yard
wait
165. left
166.
167.
168.
169. face
eyes
170.
171.
172. tinker
mend
173. pots
pleasant
174. dance
fairy
175.
176. sad
grow
177. fell
dark